*For those who choose*

Within infinite myths lies an eternal truth
Who knows it all?
Varuna has but a thousand eyes
Indra, a hundred
You and I, only two.

# Contents

## Introduction
# The Story of Ravana, Ram or Sita?

Once upon a time, there was a man called Ravana, also known as Paulatsya—being the descendent of Rishi Pulatsya, from his mother's side. He was king of Lanka and ruler of the rakshasas, who tricked a princess called Sita, dragged her out of her house in the forest and made her prisoner in his palace. He was killed by Sita's husband, Ram, the sun-prince. This story is called the Pulatsya Vadham, or the killing of the descendent of Pulatsya.

The story of Ravana's killing is part of a longer tale called the Ramayana, which tells the story of Ram from his birth to his death. However, in the din of Ravana's cruelty and Ram's valour, something is often overlooked—the story of Sita, the girl who chose.

Valmiki, author of the Ramayana, written over 2000 years ago, tells us how Sita is different from Ram and Ravana. Ravana does not care for other people's choices, while Ram never makes a choice as, being the eldest son of a royal family, he is always expected to follow the rules. But Sita — she makes five choices. And had Sita not made these choices, the story of Ram would have been very different indeed. That is why Valmiki sometimes refers to the Ramayana as the Sita Charitam, the story of Sita.

- 2000 years ago, Valmiki wrote the Ramayana in Sanskrit.

  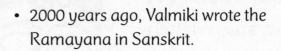

  - 1800 years ago, Jains wrote their versions of the Ramayana in Prakrit.

  - 1600 years ago, the Ramayana became part of many Sanskrit plays.

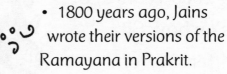

- 1400 years ago, the Ramayana reached South East Asia, thanks to storytelling sailors and merchants.

- 1000 years ago, Kamban retold the Ramayana in Tamil.

- 400 years ago, the Ramayana was being retold in Telugu, Odia, Bengali, Assamese, Malayalam, Kannada, Marathi and Hindi.

- 150 years ago, Valmiki's Ramayana was translated into English for the first time.

The Ramayana sure has a long history!

The Story of Ravana, Ram or Sita?

 # Her First Choice

Shiva, who sits on Mount Kailash, and from whose locks flows the Ganga, had a bow called Pinaka. It was a magnificient bow with which Shiva had brought down the three flying cities of asuras using a single arrow.

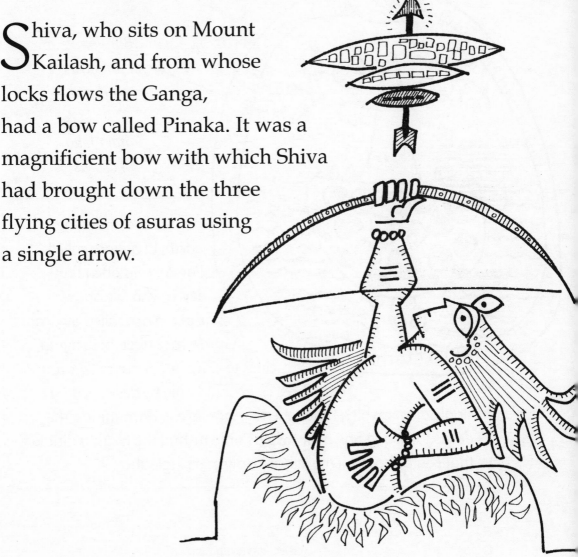

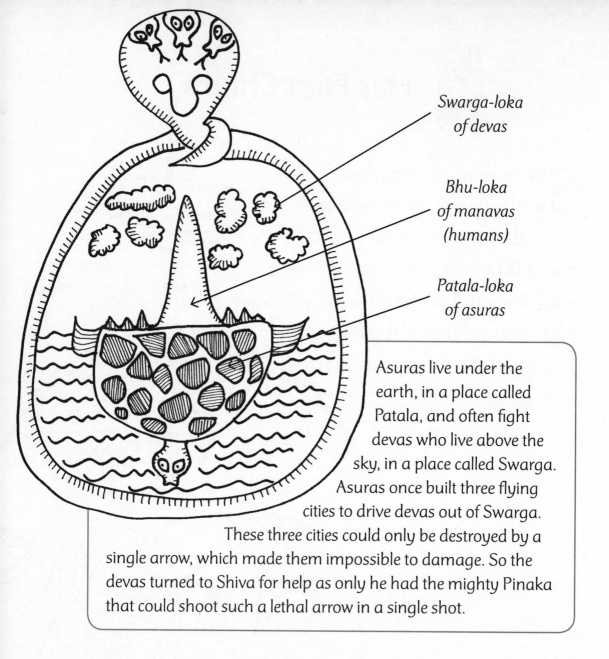

Swarga-loka
of devas

Bhu-loka
of manavas
(humans)

Patala-loka
of asuras

Asuras live under the earth, in a place called Patala, and often fight devas who live above the sky, in a place called Swarga. Asuras once built three flying cities to drive devas out of Swarga. These three cities could only be destroyed by a single arrow, which made them impossible to damage. So the devas turned to Shiva for help as only he had the mighty Pinaka that could shoot such a lethal arrow in a single shot.

The Girl Who Chose

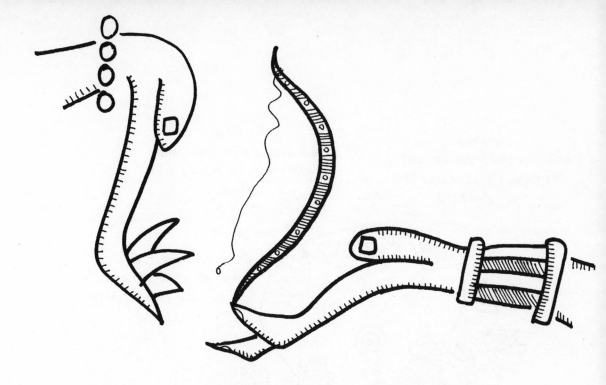

Shiva handed over this bow to Janaka, king of
Mithila. But it was too heavy for any human to lift.

'Don't worry,' said Shiva. 'Your daughter will
lift this bow and your son-in-law will string it. For
they will be the avatars of Lakshmi and Vishnu.
Vishnu has already taken birth as Ram in the house
of Dasharatha, the sun-king of the sun-city, Ayodhya.
Lakshmi is yet to be born in your house.'

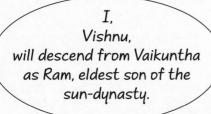

I,
Vishnu,
will descend from Vaikuntha
as Ram, eldest son of the
sun-dynasty.

I,
Adi Sesha,
will descend as Lakshman,
and serve both Sita and
Ram.

I,
Lakshmi,
will rise from the earth
as Sita, daughter of
Janaka.

Lakshmi is the goddess of wealth and Vishnu is her protector. Vishnu often takes a human form. He is born in this form, and eventually dies. This mortal form of an immortal being is known as avatar.

8

Every year, the people of
Mithila would till their fields and
sow their seeds before the rains, and
harvest the crops after. The king would
be invited to do the first
tilling of the field using a
golden plough. That year,
as Janaka was ploughing, he hit an
obstacle. Was it a rock?

Janaka dug the earth and
found a pot, and in the pot, a
little girl. He was thrilled to
see her.

'Is this the daughter Shiva
had spoken about?' he wondered.
'I shall call her Sita. She will be
my earth-princess.'

Her First Choice

After Sita came into Janaka's life, Janaka's wife gave birth to a baby girl, called Urmila, and Janaka's brother's wife gave birth to two other girls, Mandavi and Shrutakirti. Mithila was a happy place with four princesses. And just as Shiva had said, Sita alone could lift Shiva's bow. No one else could.

The Girl Who Chose

Many years later, a rishi
called Vishwamitra came
to Mithila. He brought
with him two young men,
Ram and his younger
brother, Lakshman. They
were two of Dasharatha's
four sons. The other two—
Bharata and Shatrughna—
had stayed back in the palace,
as their father did not like all
his four sons being exposed to the
dangerous rakshasas of the forest.

Rishis live in the forest, appreciating nature, plants and animals. They believe that humans should control the earth with farming and the mind with rules. The rakshasas disagree. Hence, the conflict between rishis and rakshasas.

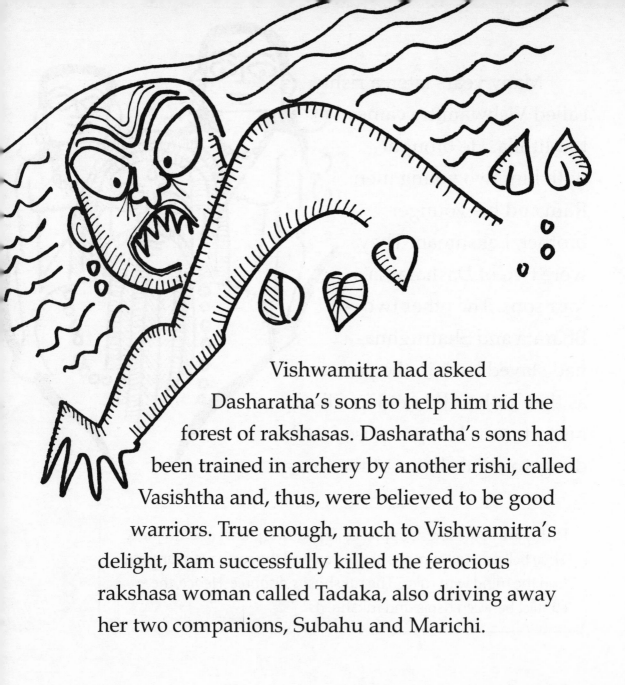

Vishwamitra had asked
Dasharatha's sons to help him rid the
forest of rakshasas. Dasharatha's sons had
been trained in archery by another rishi, called
Vasishtha and, thus, were believed to be good
warriors. True enough, much to Vishwamitra's
delight, Ram successfully killed the ferocious
rakshasa woman called Tadaka, also driving away
her two companions, Subahu and Marichi.

12

Vishwamitra then took Ram to another hermitage in the forest and pointed to a stone there. 'This was once a woman called Ahalya. She was wife to a rishi named Gautama. He saw her in the arms of Indra, king of the gods, and was so upset that he cursed her to turn into stone. It was a rash response and one that Gautama regretted, for now he could not reverse the curse to bring back his beloved wife. Can you reverse it for him, Ram? You, who took life of Tadaka — can you give Ahalya her life back?'

Ram understood clearly that forgiveness was better than punishment. So he touched the stone and wished for Ahalya to come back to life. And lo and behold! She did! Her joy knew no bounds. Gautama was happy too, as was Indra.

News of this radiant sun-prince, who killed Tadaka and liberated Ahalya, had reached Mithila even before the arrival of Ram. Janaka invited Ram, his brother and the sage Vishwamitra to his city. Maybe Ram was the prince who could string Shiva's bow and be his son-in-law, as Shiva had foretold long ago. To everyone's amazement, Ram picked up Shiva's bow easily. Not just that, he also bent the bow to string it, as he was asked to. Only, he bent it too hard and it broke!

Hearing the sound of the bow breaking, a sage called Parashurama rushed to Mithila.

'If you can break Shiva's bow, then you must be

Vishnu on earth.
Are you Vishnu?'
he asked Ram.

Ram did
not know what to say.
Parashurama handed Ram a bow, saying, 'If you can
hold my bow, it means that you are Vishnu. And that
the woman you are about to marry, Janaka's daughter
Sita, is Lakshmi.'

And sure enough, Ram picked up Parashurama's
bow, who smiled. 'Blessed is the earth, for now Ram is
here!' he exclaimed.

16

The Girl Who Chose

Janaka was happy to hand his daughter to Ram in marriage. Sita's sisters married Ram's brothers—Lakshman married Urmila, Bharata married Mandavi, Shatrughna married Shrutakirti.

They all went to live together in the big palace in Ayodhya, where they were welcomed by Dasharatha, and his three queens— Kaushalya, Sumitra and Kaikeyi.

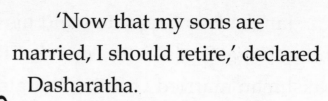

'Now that my sons are married, I should retire,' declared Dasharatha.

'I should crown Ram king and he can take care of Ayodhya with his brothers. With Janaka's daughters by their side, they will surely be good guardians of the sun-city.'

But there was a problem. Kaikeyi, Bharata's mother, was not pleased to see that Dasharatha was going to make crown-prince Ram the heir to the throne. She wanted her son to be the new king of Ayodhya.

The Girl Who Chose

Her maid,
Manthara told her,
'If Kaushalya's
son becomes
king, then your
son will be his
servant and
you will be
the mother of
a servant.'

Kaikeyi did not like this at all.

In the Mahabharata, the sage Markandeya tells the story of Ram to Yudhishthira. It is called the Ramopakhyana. Here, Brahma directs a celestial being, known as agandharva, to take birth as Manthara, and goad Kaikeyi into asking Dasharatha for two boons. It was all part of a big plan to get Ram to go to the forest and kill the rakshasa-king, Ravana.

So Kaikeyi reminded Dasharatha of the two boons he had offered her a long time ago, when she'd saved his life in battle.

'I want my son, Bharata, to be crowned king of Ayodhya. And I want Ram to go and live in the forest for fourteen years.'

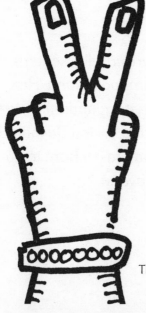

Dasharatha protested. But a promise was a promise.

The Girl Who Chose

The rulers of the sun-city were called the sun-kings because they dazzled by virtue of always following the rules of the land. If the rule said that a king must always keep his promise, then the promise would be kept. When Ram learnt of what his stepmother wanted, and of the promise made by his father, he decided to leave the kingdom immediately. The promise would be kept. The rules would be upheld. The sun-king and the sun-prince would dazzle as their ancestors did.

The sun-prince always keeps the promise made by his father, the sun-king.

Lakshman would always accompany Ram wherever he'd go. 'I will come with you,' he said, discarding his royal robes like his elder brother had, and wearing forest-dwellers' clothes, made of bark, instead.

In the Puranas, Lakshman is called Adi Sesha, the serpent with a thousand hoods, on whose coils sleeps Vishnu. The two are eternal companions.

I go where my brother goes.

'So will I,' asserted Sita.

Ram said that the forest was not a place for a woman. 'You should stay in the palace, with my parents and your sisters, and wait for my return,' he said. But Sita would not listen to him.

She said, 'You are bound by rules, but not I. I am free to choose. I choose to follow you.'

**This was Sita's first choice.**

Who will take care of Ram and Lakshman when they are in the forest? They are princes, who are used to servants, and warriors, who know how to fight. But do they know how to find water, and how to make friends with birds, beasts and bees? My sisters can look after our father-in-law, our mothers-in-law and the city of Ayodhya. I will take care of the sun-prince and his brother.

Urmila also wanted to follow her husband and her sister, but Lakshman begged her to stay.

'I will be too busy protecting Sita and Ram, and will have no time to look after you. Please understand.'

So Urmila chose to stay behind and wait for his return.

In the Telugu versions of the Ramayana, composed over 500 years ago, we hear the story of how Urmila slept through the period that her husband was in the forest. At night, she slept her share; during the day, she slept her husband's share. That way, Lakshman did not have to sleep at all in the fourteen years that he watched over Sita and Ram.

The Girl Who Chose

The whole city of Ayodhya witnessed Ram, Lakshman and Sita leave the city and enter the forest. They followed the trio to the very edge, but Ram begged them to go back. Everyone wept for the sun-prince who was bound by rules, and for the earth-princess who was free to choose.

Dasharatha could not bear the tragedy that was befalling his family. He died just as Ram entered the forest. Having lost her son and her husband, Kaushalya was inconsolable in her grief. Kaikeyi was unsure — for she then realized the horror unleashed by her ambition. Meanwhile, Sumitra tried to comfort all.

And Bharata? He refused to be king even though his mother had wished so. He was in his uncle's house when this event took place. When he returned and learned of the calamity, he rushed to the forest to bring Ram back.

The Girl Who Chose

But Ram refused to return. 'A promise is a promise. It must be kept. I must go to the forest and you must be king.'

Bharata did not like the idea of the rules being twisted to serve his mother's ambition. Rules surely existed to help people, not to hurt them. So he declared, 'As king, I renounce my kingship and restore it to my elder brother, Ram, rightful heir of the kingdom. I shall place your sandals on the throne and take care of Ayodhya as your custodian until you return.'

In the Puranas, Ram is called Maryada Purushottam, the man (purush) who is exemplary (uttam) as he respects rules and boundaries (maryada).

And so, Bharata, the man who could be king, became custodian of his brother's kingdom, refusing to live in the palace as long as his brother was away.

The Girl Who Chose

# Her Second Choice

Ram and Sita lived in the forest for thirteen years. They climbed mountains and swam across rivers. They spent the night observing the sky, the stars, and other celestial bodies, such as the planets and the comets. They spent the day observing plants, animals, fruits and roots. They met many sages on their way. They spent hours and days talking to the wise men. Thus, they discovered and learned many wondrous things.

Sita, her husband and her brother-in-law discovered in what ways animals are different from humans. Animals live by instinct. In order to survive, and to find food and mates, the strong use their strength and the weak use their intelligence. They are programmed only to help their young, or other members of their own kind. Humans, however, can help anyone — even strangers.

In the forest, there is no kindness or cruelty, no right or wrong — just the survival of the fittest.

Ram, Sita and Lakshman realized that humans use choices and rules to create a world where there is more kindness and less cruelty, more right and less wrong.

Rules are needed to make people help others.

We can choose to help people.

Helping others is the key.

The three made friends with many animals in the forest. Amongst them was an old vulture called Jatayu, who decided that he would always fly over them to ensure their safety. For the forest was a dangerous place—especially the southern landscape, below the Vindhya Mountains.

The Girl Who Chose

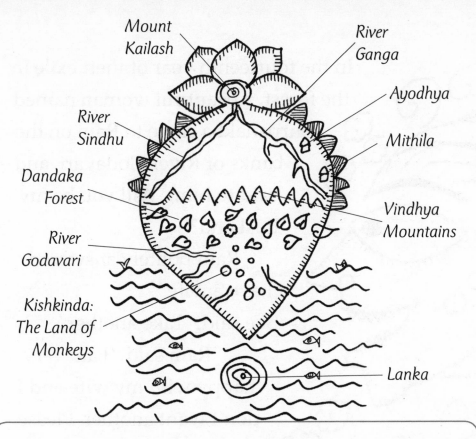

Mount Kailash

River Ganga

River Sindhu

Ayodhya

Mithila

Dandaka Forest

Vindhya Mountains

River Godavari

Kishkinda: The Land of Monkeys

Lanka

India is shaped like a diamond, with the Himalayan Mountains making up the northern border and the oceans making up the southern border. Dividing this diamond-shaped land into the north and south, is the Vindhya Range. Ayodhya is located in the north. During his exile, Ram travelled, with Sita and Lakshman, to every corner of the continent, discovering caves and ponds and rivers. These eventually became pilgrimage sites.

In the fourteenth year of their exile in the forest, a beautiful woman named Surpanakha came to Ram on the banks of River Godavari, and said to him, 'Will you be my husband?'

Ram politely answered, 'I have a wife.'

She said, 'Take another.'

Ram said, 'I am very happy with my wife and I don't want another. Please respect my choice.'

Valmiki, in his Sanskrit Ramayana, describes Surpanakha as an ugly creature with uncontrollable desires, while Kamban's Tamil Ramayana describes her as a beautiful lady and the widow of Vidyutjivha, who is accidentally killed by Ravana.

The Girl Who Chose

Surpanakha did not
like what she heard.
She felt rejected and angry.
She attacked Sita, hoping
that with her gone, Ram
would take another wife.
Clearly she was a rakshasa
who did not care for other
people's choices, but only
about her own desire. Ram
tried to stop her, but Surpanakha
would not walk away. She was
determined to do as she pleased. Finally,
an irritated Lakshman pulled out his sword and cut
off Surpanakha's nose. Yelling in pain, she ran away
into the dense dark forest.

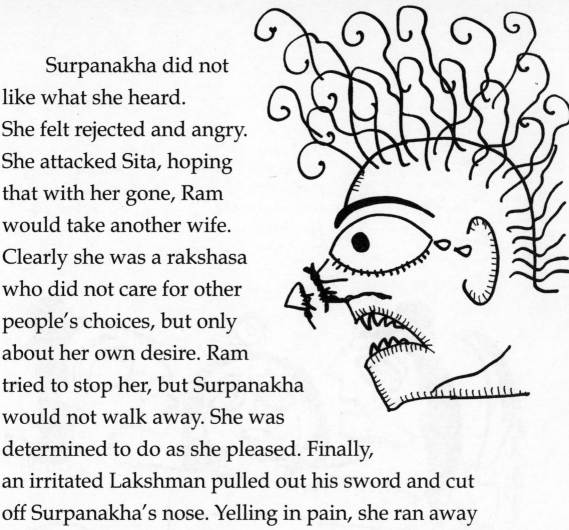

The Girl Who Chose

Soon the forest was filled with the sound of angry rakshasas—Surpanakha's brothers and companions—determined to avenge the cruelty of Ram and Lakshman. Had it not been self-defence? But it did not matter to the rakshasas. In anger, logic makes no sense. The rakshasas attacked the two brothers, who fought bravely—shooting arrows skillfully until the rakshasas retreated. 'We will be back,' they snarled as they withdrew. This made Ram and Lakshman very nervous and they always carried their weapons, guarding each other as well as Sita.

DID YOU NOTICE? Rakshasa women are always accompanied by two male companions who fight with them, and for them. Tadaka had Subahu and Maricha. Surpanakha had Khara and Dushan. Did Surpanakha consider Sita to be a rakshasa woman, just like her, for she too was accompanied by two men, Ram and Lakshman?

A few days later, Sita saw a golden deer grazing quite close to her shelter. Sita said to Ram, 'Oh what a lovely deer. I would love to pet that deer.'

Ram said, 'I will get the deer for you.'

He went into the deep forest, following the animal. For a long time, Sita and Lakshman waited to see him emerge but nothing happened.

Suddenly they heard Ram's voice, 'Lakshman, help! Lakshman, help!'

Sita panicked and asked Lakshman to go looking for him. 'He is in trouble.'

In palm-leaf paintings from ancient Odisha, the golden deer is shown as having two heads.

The Girl Who Chose

At first,
Lakshman
hesitated to
go, for Ram had instructed him
never to leave Sita alone. But
Sita insisted, accusing him of
bothering more about royal rules
than about his brother's pain.
Lakshman said, 'I will go
but before that, I will draw a line
outside your hut. You must not
cross it. You are safe inside the line;
outside the line, you are not safe.
Sita agreed and Lakshman left.

The story of Lakshman's line or the Lakshman Rekha is not found in Valmiki's Ramayana, but was invented by Krittivasa, who retold the story of Ram in Bengali over 400 years ago.

The Girl Who Chose

Soon a hermit arrived at her door.

The hermit said, 'I am hungry. Can you feed me?'

'I will feed you,' Sita replied. She went into her hut and came out with food. She offered it to him across the line, without stepping outside the boundary.

The hermit took offence. He said, 'That is not the way to serve your guest. You must walk across the line and serve me properly.'

Sita realized he was speaking to her with a humanity that separates man from animals. Animals don't consider any boundaries in the forest. Man creates them.

Sita wondered, if she stays inside, she is safe. But will it help the hermit? He will remain hungry.

And then she wondered some more. Sita had to make a choice—a choice that animals don't have. Either she could let the hermit be hungry while remaining safe herself. Or she could take a risk and step outside the rekha to feed the poor soul. Sita understood that her choice would help someone and so she decided to take the risk. In the forest, the animal only thinks about its own safety. Not about protecting another animal. This was the difference between animals and humans. Humans help other humans.

Thus, she stepped outside the line to feed the poor hermit.

**This was Sita's second choice.**

As soon as Sita crossed the line, the hermit changed into a fierce man and grabbed her by force. Sita had to pay a price for her choice; it had terrible repercussions. Her act of goodness had a bad consequence. But she considered at that moment—if she had to feed the hungry over her own safety, would she do it again? *Yes*, she said to herself.

As Sita was dragged into the man's flying vehicle called the Pushpaka Vimana, she screamed for help. But she realized that Ram and Lakshman were too far to come and save her. She panicked that Ram will not be able to trace her, but then she had an idea. As the Pushpaka Vimana rose in the air and

The Girl Who Chose

moved south, she began to drop her
jewellery one by one — her earrings, her
bangles, her gold chains, the rings on
her fingers and those on her toes.
These fell on the forest floor, creating a
trail to guide Ram.

   When Ram returned
to the hut, he discovered
that Sita was missing. He
looked around but she was
nowhere to be found. What
had happened to her? Then, not
far from the hut, he saw a wounded vulture.

Did the Ramayana inspire the European fairy tale of 'Hansel and
Gretel', who leave breadcrumbs to mark a trail from their home
as they venture into the forest? Sadly, birds eat the breadcrumbs
and the brother and sister are unable to find their way back.

Her Second Choice

It was Jatayu. His wings had been chopped off.

'She was kidnapped by Ravana, king of the rakshasas. He has taken her away on his flying chariot. They went south. I tried to stop them but Ravana cut my wings.'

Revealing this, the poor bird breathed his last. On hearing of Sita's misfortune, Ram began to weep.

What would the rakshasa-king do to her? Then he wondered how he would live without her. The pain that he felt was tremendous.

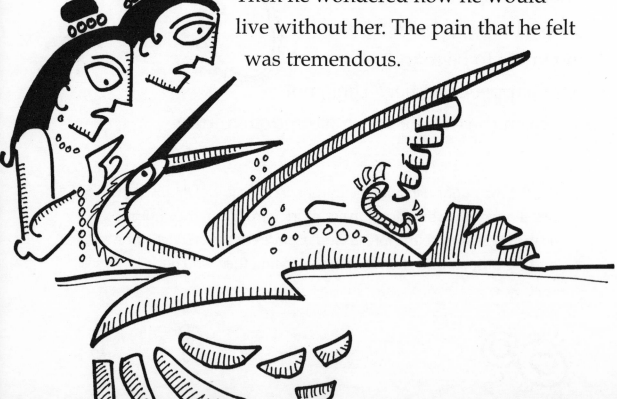

# Her Third Choice

After a long, long journey over the sea, Sita found herself on the island of Lanka, under an Ashoka tree in a garden at Ravana's palace. The whole city was made of gold. The palace, also of gold, was guarded by female rakshasas.

'Why don't you want to marry our Lord?' they asked angrily. 'He is handsome, rich, smart, talented, powerful, feared and clearly very fond of you. He has even offered to make you his queen. Yet you refuse. Why?'

Very calmly, Sita replied, 'I was given in marriage to Ram. That is why I am his wife. I will always be his wife. There is no choice here; there are rules in place.

The Girl Who Chose

Your king refuses to understand these rules, because he is consumed by desire. If he truly cared for me, he would let me follow the rules I should follow as the wife of the sun-prince, and not keep me prisoner.'

The women of Lanka thought about what she said. And they agreed that Ravana was, in fact, trying to enforce his will on her.

They asked Sita, 'What will you do? Your husband is far away. You are in the middle of the forest, on an island surrounded by sea, which is full of monsters.'

Sita replied, 'I will wait. For I have faith in my husband. One day he will come.'

While Sita waited, the women told her about how the rakshasas had descended from Brahma.

'Brahma, the creator, had a son called Kashyapa who had many wives and from whom were born the devas, the asuras, the humans, the birds, the fishes, the serpents and the animals of the forest. He had another son, called Pulatsya, from whose wives descended the yakshas and the rakshasas, who live in the forest.'

Asuras are not the same as rakshasas. Asuras are Kashyapa's children while rakshasas are Pulatsya's. Asuras live under the earth and they fight devas who live above the sky. Rakshasas live in the forest, follow the law of the jungle, and fight humans who live in civilized societies.

The Girl Who Chose

51

They told Sita about the birth of Ravana and his
rivalry with his stepbrother, Kubera.

'A rishi called Vaishrava married two women,
a yaksha and a rakashasa. The yaksha woman gave
birth to Kubera and the rakshasa woman gave birth
to Ravana. Kubera was rich, successful, and talented.
He built the golden city of Lanka on an island in
the middle of the sea, and invented the Pushpaka
Vimana. Ravana became jealous of Kubera and after

praying to the gods, acquired many powers using which he drove Kubera and his yakshas away, made himself king of Lanka and claimed the Pushpaka Vimana for himself. Now poor Kubera lives somewhere in the north, in a city called Alaka.'

Sita was not impressed. 'My Ram gives his kingdom away to his brother, Bharata. And your Ravana drives Kubera away from his own kingdom.'

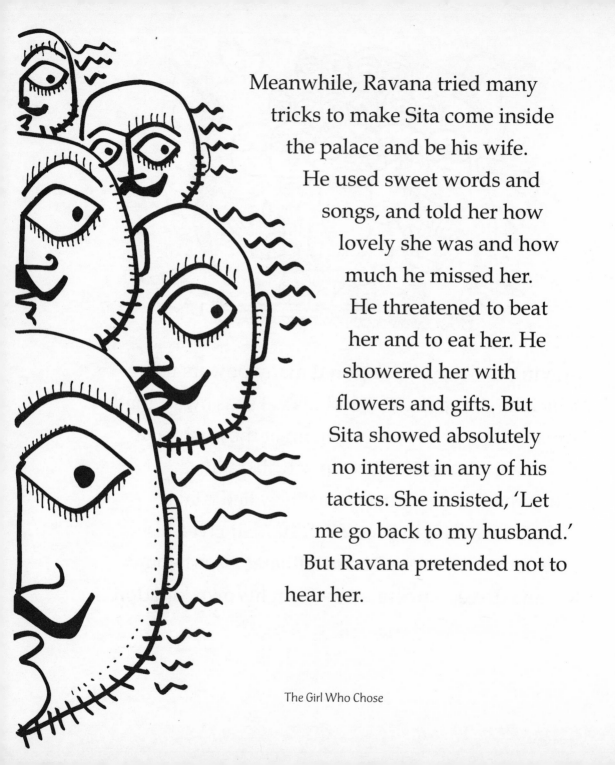

Meanwhile, Ravana tried many
tricks to make Sita come inside
the palace and be his wife.
He used sweet words and
songs, and told her how
lovely she was and how
much he missed her.
He threatened to beat
her and to eat her. He
showered her with
flowers and gifts. But
Sita showed absolutely
no interest in any of his
tactics. She insisted, 'Let
me go back to my husband.'
But Ravana pretended not to
hear her.

The Girl Who Chose

Months passed, the rains came and went. One
night, when the rakshasa women guarding Sita were
asleep and snoring, something fell from the branches
above, right in front of her. It was too shiny to be
a fruit. She picked it up and found it was a ring—
Ram's ring! She recognized it and looked up. There
was a monkey sitting on the branches.

The monkey jumped
down and bowing
to her, said, 'I am
Hanuman, born
by the grace of
the wind-god,
Vayu. My mother
is Anjani and my
father is Kesari.
I serve Sugriva,
king of Kishkinda,
and on his orders, I have
come here as messenger of
your husband, Ram.'

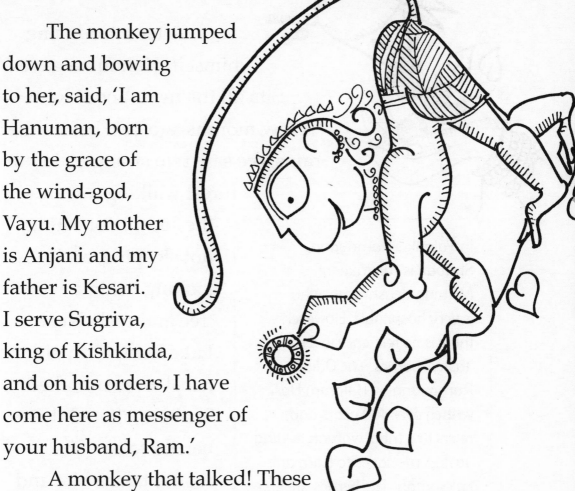

A monkey that talked! These
were the famous vanaras she had
heard of — those who lived deep in the jungle in
the south.

After introducing himself, Hanuman gave Sita all the news about Ram. 'A few months ago, just before the rains, we saw two strangers in our forest walking towards the south, not eating, not sleeping, and looking behind every tree and rock. Near Lake Pampa, an old tribal woman, called Shabari, offered them berries to eat. She would take a bite and offer only the sweetest. Only Ram accepted this. Not Lakshman.'

In Valmiki's Ramayana, Shabari is caretaker of Matanga's ashrama, who is very hospitable. However, there is no reference to feeding 'tasted' berries. The Odia Ramayana by Balaram Das, written over 400 years ago, refers to a tribal woman feeding 'tasted' mangoes to Ram and Lakshman. The berries are first referred to 300 years ago, in *Bhakti-Rasa-Bodhini*, written in Hindi by Priyadas.

Hanuman continued, 'Being curious, I introduced myself. Then, realizing that they posed no threat, I took them to meet my king, Sugriva. Ram told us that he was looking for his wife, Sita, who had been abducted by Ravana and taken to the south. We knew of the abduction for we had seen Ravana flying south in his chariot, a wailing woman in his arms. We showed Ram the trail of jewellery you had left behind. Ram then asked Sugriva for help in finding you. Sugriva said he would, but only if Ram helped him overpower his brother Vali and establish him as king of Kishkinda instead.'

The Ramayana describes various vanaras as the sons of Vedic gods. Hanuman is the wind-god Vayu's son, Sugriva is the sun-god Surya's son and Vali is the rain-god Indra's son.

'Vali and Sugriva were the twin sons of Riksha, former king of Kishkinda. Before dying, Riksha instructed the brothers to share rule of the kingdom. Unfortunately, Vali did not trust Sugriva and following a minor misunderstanding, drove him out of Kishkinda. The only way to reclaim the kingdom was by killing Vali. Sugriva told Ram, "I will challenge my brother to a duel and when we are fighting, you should shoot an arrow from behind the bushes and strike Vali dead." Ram agreed. He advised Sugriva to wear a garland around his neck to distinguish himself, for the two of them looked very alike. So, garland around his neck, Sugriva challenged Vali to a duel and while they were fighting, Ram's arrow struck

Surya taught Hanuman the Vedas, which is why Hanuman was well versed in Sanskrit. As tuition fee, Surya asked Hanuman to protect Sugriva.

The Girl Who Chose

and killed Vali, which made Sugriva the undisputed king of the vanaras.'

Shooting Vali with an arrow from behind the bushes while he was engaged in fighting Sugriva — is that not cheating, wondered Sita.

Hanuman continued, 'It was Sugriva's fight, not Ram's. Vali had used strength to drive Sugriva out. Sugriva could only use cunning to overpower his mighty brother. Ram was just his instrument; he was just following Sugriva's instructions. Besides, if Ram had attacked Vali from the front, then the vanaras would deem him their king, not Sugriva.'

'After becoming king,' said Hanuman, 'Sugriva kept his end of the promise. He asked me to travel south and search for you. This meant crossing many mountains and rivers and forests—and finally, a great sea, full of monsters. It was not easy but here I am, ready to take you back to your husband. For I am no ordinary vanara; I can leap across the ocean. So please jump on my back and I will return you to Ram.'

The Ramayana describes Hanuman's journey across the sea, during which he cunningly outwits the sea-monster, called Surasa, and kills another sea-monster, called Simhika—finally defeating Lankini, the goddess who guards Lanka. This part of the Ramayana, called Sundara Kanda, is very popular amongst devotees.

The Girl Who Chose

Sita replied, 'Thank you, Hanuman, for offering to help. But I want my husband to cross the sea, come to Lanka, kill Ravana and rescue me himself, thus restoring the reputation of his family. For Ram is a prince, and royal reputations matter a lot to princes, especially to those who belong to the sun-dynasty.'

**This was Sita's third choice.**

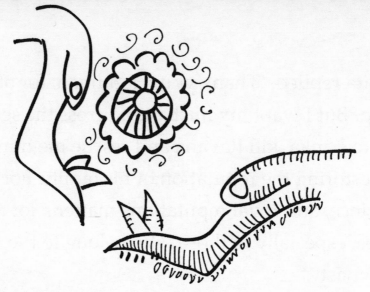

Strange are the ways of humans, thought Hanuman, but he respected Sita's choice. 'Please give me something of yours that I can present to your husband, so that he believes that I had actually found you,' requested Hanuman. Sita gave Hanuman the only piece of jewellery she had left—her hairpin, known in Sanskrit as *chuda-mani*.

> In the forest, Ram and Lakshman wore clothes of bark, as hermits are supposed to. But not Sita, who wore a lot of jewellery—as princesses did in ancient times.

The Girl Who Chose

Then Hanuman said, 'I have travelled so far, and that has made me very hungry. Can I get something to eat?'

Sita replied, 'This garden is full of fruits; eat whatever you like.'

Hanuman jumped from tree to tree, eating and enjoying himself. After he'd had his fill, he began to shake the branches and trees, wreaking havoc in the garden. The female rakshasas of the garden woke up with a start and seeing the monkey, ran out in a fright and called the guards.

The guards came in and, after a great fight, managed to catch Hanuman (or did he let them?). They dragged him by his tail to Ravana.

Ravana looked at him and quizzed, 'Who are you?'

In many folk versions of the Ramayana, known as Rama-kathas, Hanuman lengthens his tail and coils it around to make a throne on which he sits, while talking to Ravana. His tail-throne is taller than Ravana's so that he can look down upon the rakshasa-king.

Hanuman smiled and announced, 'I am Ram's messenger and I have flown across the sea to tell you that Ram is on his way to get his wife back. Now let me go. Is this the way to treat messengers in your kingdom?

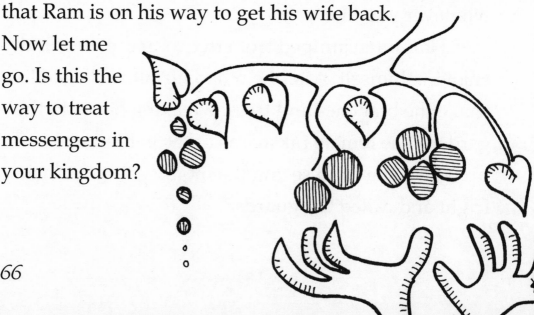

Ravana was not amused.
He decided to teach the
mischievous monkey a lesson.

'Light his tail on fire!',
he ordered.

Hanuman pretended to
be afraid, but as soon as the
guards set his tail on fire, he
escaped their clutches and,
laughing all the while, began
jumping from roof to roof,
house to house — burning
the palace and the city with
his tail. The only spot that
Hanuman did not burn was
the Ashoka-garden where Sita
was seated.

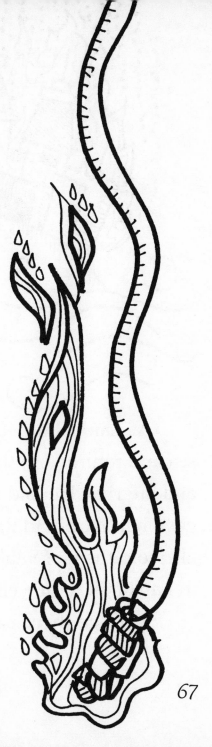

As Lanka burned, Hanuman leapt across the sea and returned to the forest, where he found Ram and Sugriva. He told them of Sita's whereabouts and gave her hairpin to Ram as proof of his discovery. He also told them of Sita's choice — that she would wait in Lanka till Ram went to her rescue.

'Let's go then,' said Ram.

With Sugriva's help, he raised an army of monkeys and bears, and this great army of animals made its way to the south. On reaching the southern shores, Ram raised his bow and threatened to hurt Varuna, the sea-god, if he did not part his waters and let his army pass.

Varuna appeared before Ram and said, 'If I do that, then many fish will die. It would be better if you build a bridge across the sea. The fish will keep the stones afloat.'

'Then let's do it,' said Ram. Directed by Hanuman, the monkeys scoured the land for rocks. They threw the rocks into the sea. The fish held up the stones. Together, they were doing something that no one had ever done before—building a bridge to Lanka.

In Valmiki's Ramayana, the bridge is built under the supervision of a monkey called Nala, son of the Vedic god of architects, Vishwakarma. Tulsidas says that it was created by two monkey brothers, Nala and Nila. But in stories that have been told in the last 200 years, Hanuman plays a key role in building the bridge, writing Ram's name on the stones to ensure that they float and don't sink.

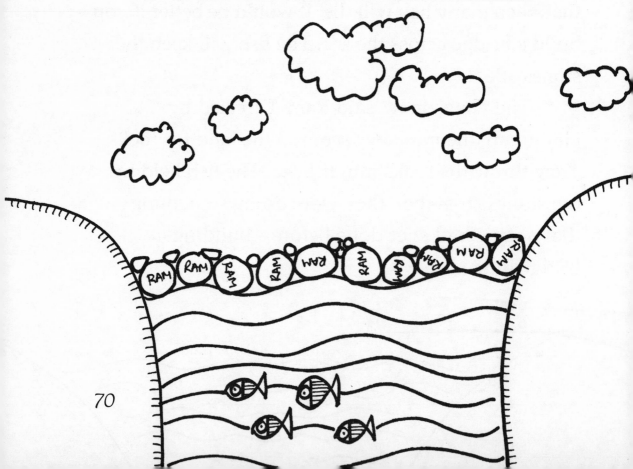

# Her Fourth Choice

The bridge was built. And the army of monkeys, led by Ram, reached the island-kingdom of Lanka. When Sita heard the news, a smile broke on her lips. Her wait was finally over.

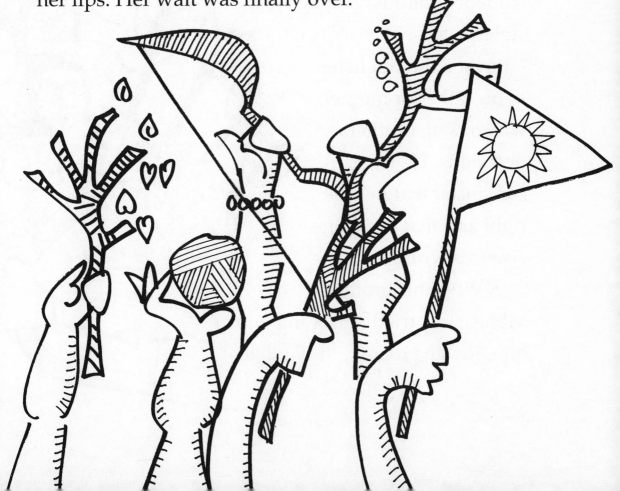

The beating of war drums filled the air.

The rakshasas looked at their king and wondered, is it not better to simply let Sita return to her husband and prevent this bloodshed?

But Ravana was not inclined towards peace. All he wanted was to possess Sita, like a stubborn child who clings to a stolen toy.

Ravana did not listen to his father or mother, wife or son, brothers or friends. He was convinced that he was right and that everyone else was wrong.

When his brother, Vibhishana, tried reasoning with him, Ravana roared, 'If you like

Ram so much, then leave this kingdom of mine.'

So Vibhishana left the palace and went over to Ram to offer his support.

*Son, peace is better than war.*

*Brother, let Sita go to her husband. Or I will leave Lanka.*

*Brother, maybe things have gone too far.*

Her Fourth Choice

The battle between the rakshasas and the vanaras was fierce. Many of Ravana's sons died, including the brave Meghanadh, also known as Indrajit.

The first Kannada film, *Sati Sulochana*, narrates the folklore, popular in the Deccan region, of how Meghanadh's wife, Sulochana, bravely recovers the dead body of her husband from the enemy camp.

Father, you are in the wrong but I will fight for you.

Many of Ravana's brothers died, including Kumbhakarna. But Ravana refused to change his mind.

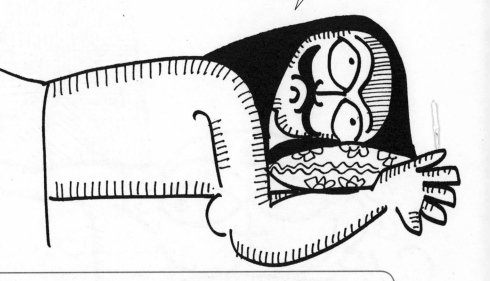

Brother, I would rather sleep. Let Sita go.

Kumbhakarna would sleep for six months at a time and then wake up for a day. On that day, he would be invincible in battle. An impatient Ravana, however, woke him up before his sleep could be completed, which is why Ram was able to kill him.

It was not easy for Ram either. Once, Lakshman was shot with a poisonous arrow. Hanuman flew north and brought back a mountain, on which grew a medicinal herb, called Sanjivani, that saved Lakshman's life.

The Girl Who Chose

Another time, Ram and Lakshman were abducted by Ravana's sorcerer-friend, Mahiravana, and his son, Ahiravana. Hanuman entered Patala, the land under the earth which is full of nagas and asuras, and he fought the sorcerers, successfully rescuing Ram and his brother.

The story of Hanuman's subterranean adventures is part of the Sanskrit work, Adbhuta Ramayana, composed 400 years ago, and has led to the worship of Patali Hanuman.

Though Hanuman was strong and capable of killing all the rakshasas by himself, he remembered that Sita wanted Ram to liberate her from Ravana's clutches himself. He respected that and offered his shoulders for Ram to ride on. Seated on Hanuman's shoulders, bow in hand, Ram finally confronted Ravana when the latter entered the battlefield on his great chariot. It was the first time they'd met.

DID YOU KNOW? Both Ram and Ravana worship Shiva and Shakti. But while Ram fights for his family and his people, Ravana fights only for himself.

It was a brutal fight, the fight between Ram and Ravana. Arrows flew from either side. The vanaras and rakshasas stopped to watch the two warriors fight — Ram to save Sita, and Ravana to keep Sita. Finally, Ram's arrow hit Ravana's navel — the spot where his life was secured — and collapsing on the ground, Ravana died. The monkeys cheered the victory. Conch shells were blown to announce the end of the war. Ram and Lakshman were happy — Sita was liberated.

Ram asked Ravana, while the latter lay dying, what had been the greatest lesson he had learnt in life. Ravana replied, 'We always chase the things that are bad for us, and avoid the things that are good.'

As Sita was leaving the Ashoka-garden, she felt excited to meet her husband. They had been separated for several months. However, when she met Ram, she was in for a great shock.

Ram said, 'I have defeated the man who had kidnapped the queen of Ayodhya, the daughter-in-law of my family. And, therefore, I have saved my family's reputation. Now, Sita, you are free to go wherever you wish.'

She responded, 'I want to go back with you.'

**This was Sita's fourth choice.**

Ram argued, 'But people will say that you have been in the house of another man — a man who was smarter as he'd had ten heads, who was stronger as he'd had twenty hands, a man who went around the world on a flying chariot.'

So Sita said, 'I will walk on fire to prove my love for you. If I have truly loved you and no one else, then the flames of the fire will not hurt me.'

Saying so, Sita stepped into the fire. The flames did not even touch her.

Ram was overjoyed.

When Ram, Lakshmana and Sita decided to
return, Vibhishana, the new king of Lanka, suggested,
'Why don't you use Ravana's vimana? It's faster.'

After Vali's death, Sugriva married Vali's widow, Tara, before
becoming king of Kishkinda. After Ravana's death, Vibhishana
married Ravana's widow, Mandodari, before becoming king of
Lanka. They all attended Ram's coronation.

The Girl Who Chose

# Her Fifth Choice

On their return, Ram was crowned king of Ayodhya and Sita, his queen. They lived in a beautiful palace along with Ram's brothers and their wives, Sita's sisters. Hanuman lived in the palace too, as Ram's messenger. Both king and his subjects respected the rules of the land. Everyone was aware of their duties. Everything was orderly. The kingdom was bustling with prosperity. Everyone felt safe and happy.

Tulsidas's famous Ramayana, written in Awadhi (old Hindi) over 400 years ago and known as *Ram-charit-manas*, ends with the arrival of Ram from Lanka and his coronation as king of Ayodhya.

The Girl Who Chose

But nothing lasts forever. Not even peace. Gossip started going around the streets. People remembered that Sita had lived away from her husband in Lanka, under Ravana's shadow, for a long time.

'She is not pure,' they said. 'How can our perfect king have an imperfect queen?' they wondered.

The royal washerman was heard saying, 'I can clean stains from royal clothes. But I cannot clean the stain on the royal reputation.'

In Valmiki's Ramayana, the street is abuzz with gossip. But in Krittivasa's Bengali Ramayana, the gossip is started by the washerman.

The women of the palace became jealous of Ram's love for Sita. They decided to sow doubts in his mind about Sita's love for him. They kept asking Sita to describe Ravana.

'I never saw his face. I only saw his shadow,' she said.

They asked her to draw the rakshasa-king's shadow. She did, and the women let out a gasp!

They told everyone that Sita still thought about Ravana.

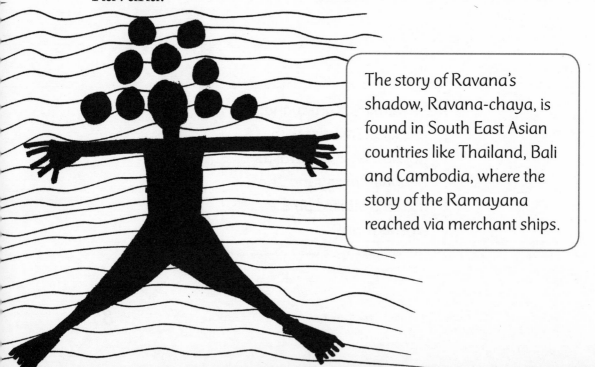

The story of Ravana's shadow, Ravana-chaya, is found in South East Asian countries like Thailand, Bali and Cambodia, where the story of the Ramayana reached via merchant ships.

When Ram learned that everyone in the city was gossiping about Sita, he was alarmed. The rules were clear — anything that stained the royal reputation had to be removed. Sita had to go. He told Lakshman to take Sita to the forest and leave her there. Lakshman protested at first but then obeyed the sun-king.

When they reached the forest, Lakshman told Sita, 'My brother has told me to leave you here. You are no longer welcome in the sun-city.'

When Sita asked why, Lakshman said that he was simply following the royal command. And so should she.

Sita realized that this time, she had no choice. She was being told to obey. If someone had asked her, what would she have chosen? To stay in the kingdom that did not want her? Or to step out and live in the forest which did not reject her?

Sita knew that she would be okay in the forest. Had she not spent fourteen years there with Ram? She knew how to find food. She knew how to find water. She knew how to find shelter. She even knew how to pass the time. She enjoyed the rivers, the mountains, the birds, the animals, the butterflies and

The Girl Who Chose

the stars. The sages in the forest would provide her company. And when they were not around, she could surely manage by herself. But she wasn't by herself.

She hadn't told her husband that she was soon going to be a mother — she was carrying his child inside her. A few months later, she gave birth to Ram's child — children, rather. They were twins! She named them Luv and Kush.

Many folk Ramayanas say that Sita had only one son called Luv, whom she had left in Valmiki's care when she'd gone to fetch water. But the child went missing and so, an anxious Valmiki turned a bundle of kusha grass into the very likeness of Luv. Thus was Kush created.

The Girl Who Chose

For the next few years, mother and sons lived peacefully in the forest with great joy. They met the sages of the forest and learnt many things. The children grew up eating berries and fruits, and were kind to the animals. They made friends with deer and tigers and elephants. Sita taught them how to use the bow and arrow.

The poet-sage Valmiki had composed an epic poem on the life of Ram. Sita told him to teach the song to her children. She did not tell Valmiki who she was, or who her children were. She wanted to keep their identities secret, but she did want Luv and Kush to learn about their father.

When Luv and Kush had learnt the poem, which they sang beautifully, Valmiki asked the children, 'Would you like to sing it in the court of Ram?' They agreed enthusiastically.

So Valmiki took them to the king's court in the

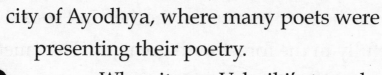

city of Ayodhya, where many poets were presenting their poetry.

When it was Valmiki's turn, he announced, 'I have composed a work based on Ram's story and these two boys will sing it.'

Luv and Kush's performance was appreciated by all, including Ram, who did not recognize his own children.

He asked the two boys, 'What reward would you like for that beautiful performance?'

Luv and Kush answered that they wanted to see the famous queen, Sita, who Ram had rescued from the clutches of Ravana.

DID YOU KNOW? In Kerala, people spend the month of Karkidakam, that falls in the middle of the rainy season, reading the Ramayana. Kerala has the unique distinction of having four temples, one dedicated to Ram, Lakshman, Bharata and Shatrughna each.

Ram showed them a doll in his hand—a doll made of gold. 'This is the only Sita I have now.'

Luv and Kush were shocked. A doll!

Ram explained that the people of Ayodhya felt that the sun-prince could not have a wife who had lived in the shadow of Ravana. So he'd had to send her to the forest, where she lived alone while he lived with this golden doll for company. The children could not understand this. 'But what was her crime?'

DID YOU NOTICE? In the Ramayana, gold appears again and again—the golden plough of Janaka, the golden deer, the golden city of Lanka, the golden statue of Sita.

The Girl Who Chose

Ram explained that the rules of the sun-dynasty were strict—any member of the royal family, whose character was doubted by the people of the sun-city, had to be cast away without a moment's thought.

The children argued, 'But that is so unfair.'

Ram exclaimed, 'It is not about right or wrong, fair or unfair. It is about rules.'

Luv and Kush ran out of the palace. They no longer liked Ram. They told their mother that Ram was not a good man. Sita felt terrible.

She told her children, 'Some people have the freedom to choose. Others don't and they have to follow the rules. The world is full of all kinds of people.'

I abandoned the queen of soiled reputation as per the rules of the land. But I did not abandon my wife, Sita. Therefore, I've never remarried.

One day, a regal white horse entered the forest. There was a cloth-sign on the horse which stated that wherever the horse would graze, that land would come under the command of Ram, king of Ayodhya.

The Girl Who Chose

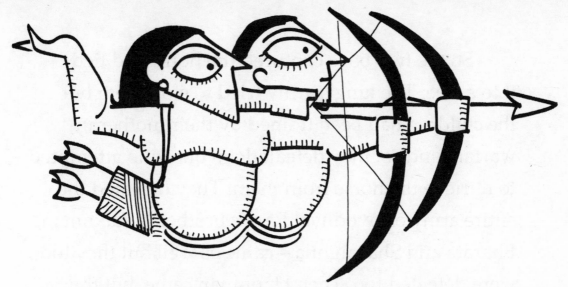

Luv said to Kush, 'If we let the horse pass through our house, we will come under the command of a king who only follows the rules. It is our choice to allow or stop that horse from making us his subjects.'

Kush agreed.

DID YOU NOTICE? The Ramayana is full of tales about brothers—Ram and his brothers, Vali and his brothers, Ravana and his brothers, Luv and Kush. But, unlike the others, Luv and Kush never fought.

So the two boys captured the horse and tied it to a tree. The king's army tried to stop them but the children had been trained by their mother in warfare and so, they defeated anyone who attempted to retrieve the horse from them. They defeated the entire army of Ayodhya! Ram's brothers — Lakhman, Bharata and Shatrughna — came as well but they too were defeated too. Then Hanuman came, but the children managed to tie him to a tree.

To save his brothers and his army, Ram himself rode into the forest.

As he raised his bow against Luv and Kush, Sita came running between them.

In the Adbhuta Ramayana, Sita is a form of the goddess Kali who can defeat demons more powerful than Ravana. Naturally her children are powerful too.

The Girl Who Chose

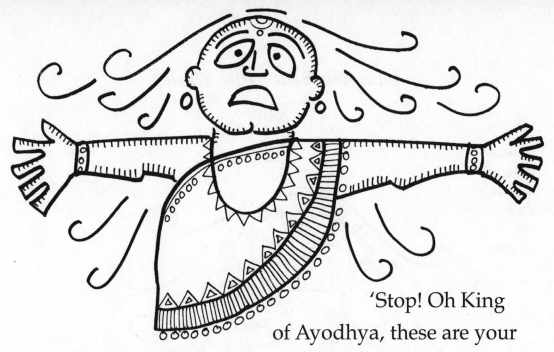

'Stop! Oh King of Ayodhya, these are your own children, and mine.'

Ram recognized Sita, and the bow fell from his hand. Ram was stunned.

'Come back,' said Ram. 'The people no longer see you as a blemish to my royal reputation. They say you are purer than gold.'

Sita said, ' I cannot come back to a city where reputation matters more than love. I will stay in the forest.'

# This was Sita's fifth choice.

I have done my best as a daughter, sister, wife and mother.

Now, it is time to go.

Ram, Ram, Ram . . . always in my heart.

Ram is called Eka-patni-vrata, a husband who has only one wife and is true to her always.

However, she told her sons to go to their father and serve the sun-city well.

Sita then called out to the earth beneath her, which opened up like a mother spreading her arms to welcome her daughter. Sita slipped into the earth's embrace.

Ram tried to catch her and pull her out, but could not. Sita was gone.

As king, I upheld the rules, and I made my kingdom happy.

As husband, I was faithful to my wife. But I did not make her happy.

DID YOU NOTICE? Ram weeps thrice in the Ramayana. First, when he learns of Sita's abduction. Second, when he tells Lakshman to take her to the forest. Third, when Sita enters the earth. Each time, the cause is his separation from Sita.

Ram looked at his sons, Luv and Kush, and said, 'Will you be able to share the kingdom and manage it well, like Bharata and I? Or will you fight like Sugriva and Vali, or Ravana and Kubera?'

The children confirmed, 'We shall share the kingdom.'

Hearing this, Ram was very happy. Sita had raised the children well.

Ram too decided that his life on earth was over. He could not live without Sita by his side. His time to return to the heavens had come. So he walked into River Sarayu and never returned.

Five hundred years ago, Raghunath Mahanta wrote the Assamese Ramayana, in which Sita misses her children and so she gets Vasuki, king of serpents, to bring them to Patala. Ram tells Hanuman to launch an attack and get them back. After a great struggle, peace is restored. Sita promises to occasionally visit earth, but secretly, only for her family.

The Girl Who Chose

Her Fifth Choice

The waters of the river mingled with the earth;
the seeds germinated. Flowers bloomed, fruits
ripened. Luv and Kush ate the fruits with relish.

The Girl Who Chose

## *Conclusion*
# The Sita inside You

In the forest, there are no choices or rules. Animals live by their instinct. The strong use strength and the weak use intelligence to survive. They cannot choose; they cannot help.

Humans can make choices. Humans can also help. Thus human society is all about choices and rules. We can choose to help or choose not to. Rules are meant to force humans to help others. When rules do not help people, we have the choice to challenge and change them.

Ravana does not care for
rules. He chooses
to do whatever
makes him
happy—choosing
war over peace,
even at the cost of his family
dying and his city burning.

Ram is obsessed with rules. He follows them even if they make him unhappy. But this is what makes Ram reliable and trustworthy. He even chooses to stay faithful to Sita, and not remarry, although the rules allow him to.

The Sita inside You

Sita makes choices. But she follows rules when they help people—such as the rule of feeding hungry people, or the rule of wives staying true to husbands despite temptation. She also breaks rules when they harm rather than help people— such as the rule that wives must stay in the house while husbands go to the forest, or the rule that says reputation is more important than the truth, or the rule that wives must obey their husbands without question.

All choices have consequences. Sita chose to cross Lakshman's line to feed a hungry man and ended up being kidnapped. Should she have followed the rules and stayed within the line? The Ramayana thus shows that it is not easy to choose, just as it can be very difficult to follow rules.

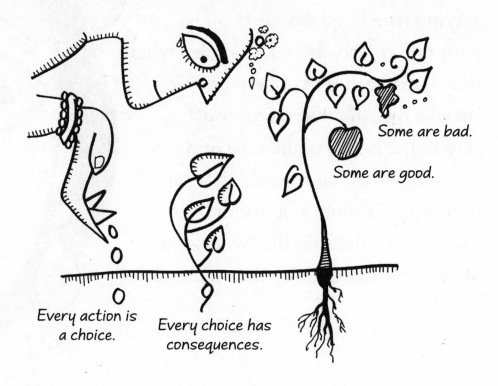

Some are bad.

Some are good.

Every action is a choice.

Every choice has consequences.

As a reader, you will find Ravana, Ram and Sita inside you. You will also find Ravana, Ram and Sita around you. Make your choice. And help others, as only humans can do.

*If you make a choice, accept all the consequences with grace.*

# More from Devdutt Pattanaik

## *Fun in Devlok Omnibus*

**Why is Indra an unhappy god?**

**Why is the cow such a cool animal?**

**Who is the demon of forgetfulness?**

Master storyteller Devdutt Pattanaik answers these curious questions and reveals many more secrets of the world of gods and demons in this delightfully illustrated omnibus, featuring all six tales in the Fun in Devlok series.

Follow Harsha as he discovers the secret to happiness, listen to Gauri's fascinating conversation with a talking cow, play dumb charades with Shiva, find out why identity cards are important even for Krishna, join the fight between Kama and Yama, and learn why the river Saraswati disappeared mysteriously.

Jump right in. The gates of Devlok are open.

# More from Devdutt Pattanaik

## *Pashu*

**A fish saves the world**

**A horse flies across the sky**

**A king discovers that his beloved wife is actually a frog**

Hindu mythology is full of tales in which animals play important roles. Some animals are looked upon with dread, while some are worshipped along with the gods. Some shape the fate of the world, others form everlasting bonds with humans.

Where did the animals come from? From Vishnu's avatars or Shiva's asanas? How was a deer responsible for the events of the Ramayana? Why is Garuda the sworn enemy of the nagas? How did a mongoose teach Yudhishtira the true meaning of sacrifice?

Devdutt Pattanaik answers all these questions and more in this exquisitely illustrated book, retelling numerous animal stories from ancient texts, with his trademark charm and wit.